Contents

ABOUT PHONICS

There are just over 40 sounds which go together to make up every single spoken word in the English language. These are called phonemes. Written words are made up of letters which represent these phonemes. In the simplest terms, phonics is linking letters - or combinations of letters - to their phonemes, or phonemes to letters.

Sometimes phonemes are single letter sounds, as in the word 'Ted' which breaks down into three: 'T-e-d'. Sometimes they are not. The word 'thing', for example, is five letters but also breaks down into three phonemes: 'th-i-ng'.

Words can be divided into two basic groups: regular phonic (words such as 'Ted') and irregular (such as 'what'). Regular words, which are far more common, can be sounded out. Irregular words have to be learned.

There are both regular and irregular words in *Ted and Friends.* These have been carefully chosen, and particular phonemes regularly repeated (for example: n-ai-l, s-n-ai-l, t-ai-l-s), so that your child will become familiar with identifying the letter combinations and sounds, and will grow in confidence. At the back of the book, you'll find a list of words used in each story, broken down into their phonemes and grouped together with words containing similar phonemes.

Read these stories with your child, encouraging your child to sound out the words as you go. Soon, most children will start to sound out the words for themselves. This is an excellent way of helping to develop an important reading skill.

Dr. Marlynne Grant

Ted and Friends

Phil Roxbee Cox
Illustrated by Stephen Cartwright
Edited by Jenny Tyler

Language consultant:
Dr. Marlynne Grant
BSc, CertEd, MEdPsych, PhD, AFBPs, CPsychol

There is a yellow duck to find on every page.

First published in 2009 by Usborne Publishing Ltd. Usborne House, 83-85 Saffron Hill, London EC1N 8RT, England.
www.usborne.com

UE. Printed in China. UE. First published in America in 2002.

Ted's shed

Don't forget there is a yellow duck to find on every page.

Meet Ted. Ted likes red.

Even Ted's shed is a red shed.

Today, Ted's bed goes into the shed.

"What are you doing, Ted?" asks Fred.

"Wait and see,"
says Ted.

Up on his stool, Ted gets down his tools.

He puts in a paw,
and pulls out
a saw.

Ted looks at his drawing.

Ted saws into a big, round log.

"What are you up to?"
asks Pup the dog.

"Wait and see," says Ted.

He saws off a big, round slice.
"This wood is good. This slice is nice."

Now Ted saws off slice after slice.

Look who's watching – a pair of mice!

Next, Ted hunts for his jar of nails.

The jar
is empty...

...apart from
a snail.

Ted and his team work on in the sun.

They huff...

...and they puff...

...but it's lots of fun!

Fred and Pup ask, "What's this all about?"

"Just wait and see!" the others shout.

Did you guess Ted's clever plan?

Ted's red shed is now a caravan!

Sam Sheep can't sleep

Don't forget there is a yellow duck to find on every page.

Sam Sheep can't sleep.

Sam Sheep gets up.

Sam Sheep wakes up Pup.

Pup barks. "It's late. It's dark."

"Go to sleep, Sam Sheep!"

"I can't sleep," says Sam Sheep.
"I need to see Fat Cat."

"Fat Cat can sleep for weeks and weeks!"

Fat Cat's on her sleeping mat in the park.
Pup barks.

"It's late. It's dark. Go to sleep!"
"Sorry," barks Pup. "Sam Sheep can't sleep."

"You need to see Ted in his red bed."

Ted is asleep in his red bed.

Pup barks in the
dark night ...

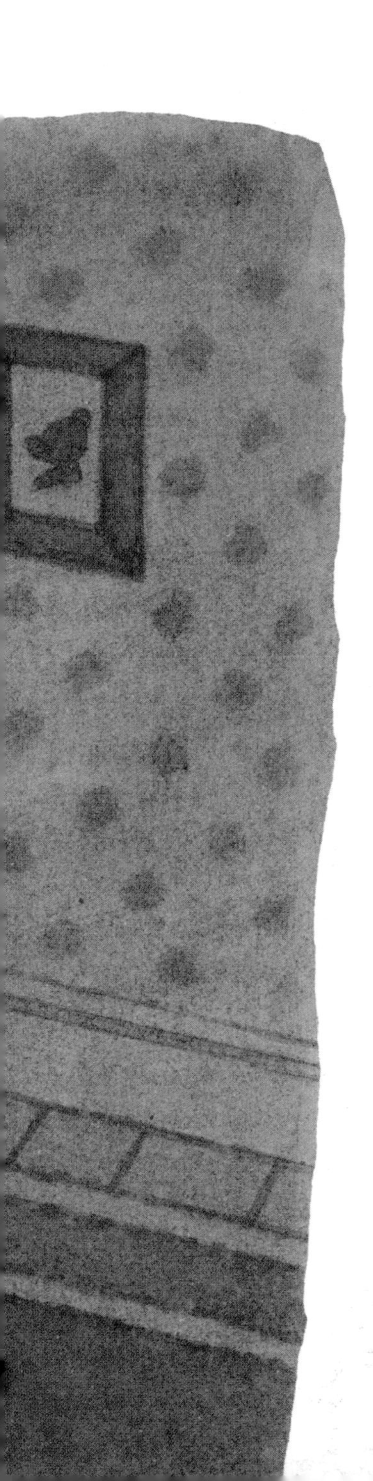

"You gave me a fright!"

"Sorry," barks Pup. "Sam Sheep can't sleep."

"Then let's see Big Pig, down the street."

Big Pig grunts "You woke me up!"
Fat Cat yawns. "Don't blame us."

"Sorry," barks Pup. "Sam Sheep can't sleep."

"Can't sleep?" says Big Pig. "Then do a jig."

"That will make you sleep, Sam Sheep."

So Pup starts to jiggle.

Fat Cat starts
to wiggle.

Ted does a wriggle.

But what about Sam Sheep?

Sam Sheep is asleep!

Fat Cat on a mat

Don't forget there is a yellow duck to find on every page.

Fat Cat sees a bee.

Fat Cat flees up a tree.
"I don't like bees!" yelps Fat Cat.

"I don't like bees
and I don't like
trees."

"I don't like bees or trees."

"Are you stuck?" shouts Big Pig.

"Bad luck!" shouts Big Pig.

Fat Cat
groans.

"I am stuck.
It *is* bad luck,"
she moans.

The tree bends...

The nest drops,
with a plop, on
top of Big Pig.

"Like my new hat, Fat Cat?"

"Good catch!"
yelps Fat Cat.

Fat Cat lands in a sandy patch.
"I must help the eggs to hatch."

Next day,

Fat Cat will not play.

"Play with me!" says Big Pig.

"Not today," says Fat Cat on her mat.

"Bake a cake with me,"
says Jake Snake.

"Not today," says Fat Cat on her mat.

"Let's run in the sun for fun," says Ted.

"Not today," says Fat Cat on her mat.

"You are lazy," says Big Pig.
"You are crazy," says Jake Snake.

"You are no fun," says Ted.

"Sssh!" says
Fat Cat.

"Stay away,"
says Fat Cat.

Clever Fat Cat!

Toad makes a road

Don't forget there is a yellow duck to find on every page.

Toad hops happily.
She has a new house on the hill.

"My new house is best," she boasts.

Toad waits and waits for the truck to bring her things.

Time ticks on...

Is the truck stuck?

Toad hops down the hill.

She's in luck.
There's the truck.

"I can't get up the hill. The load will spill."

There's no track for the truck.

So, Toad brings her things up the hill.

Toad is tired.
With one last hop
she flops into bed...

Next day, Toad eats toast.

"Today is my party!"

But only Billy the goat comes up the hill.

"It's far too steep,
except for me
or a sheep."

"What you need
is a road, Toad."

"If I need a road, then I'll make a road!" says Toad.

"But toads can't make roads,"
says Billy. "That's silly."

"Wait and see!"
says Toad.

Toad clears a track.

She then lays black, sticky tar.

She steam rollers it flat.

Toad's road is ready.

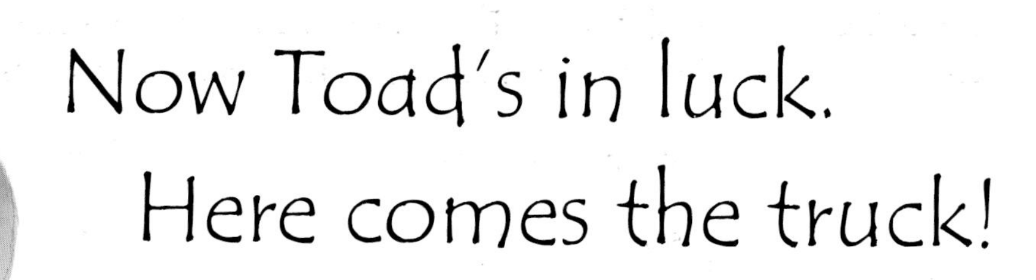

Now Toad's in luck.
Here comes the truck!

ABOUT THE WORDS IN TED'S SHED

Most words in *Ted's shed* can be broken down into single letters representing single phonemes (such as 'r-e-d' and 'b-i-g'). There are some words in this story, however, where a combination of letters creates a single phoneme, and these are listed below.

ed	sh-e-d	
eet	m-ee-t	
kes	l-(i-e)-k-s	k is an alternative spelling of the "c" sound.
me	t-(i-e)-m	
ice	s-l-(i-e)-c	i-e is an alternative spelling of the "ie" sound.
ice	n-(i-e)-c	c (before e) is an alternative spelling of the "s" sound.
ice	m-(i-e)-c	
e	s-ee	
ool	s-t-oo-l	
ols	t-oo-l-s	
own	d-ow-n	ow is an alternative spelling of the "ou" sound.
ut	ou-t	
und	r-ou-n-d	
bout	a-b-ou-t	

shout	sh-ou-t	
saw	s-aw	
drawing	d-r-aw-i-ng	
sawing	s-aw-i-ng	
saws	s-aw-s	
looks	l-oo-k-s	k is an alternative spelling of the "c" sound.
look	l-oo-k	
wood	w-oo-d	
good	g-oo-d	
start	s-t-ar-t	
off	o-ff	
this	th-i-s	
now	n-ow	
after	a-f-t-er	

for	f-or	
jar	j-ar	
wait	w-ai-t	
nails	n-ai-l-s	
snail	s-n-ai-l	
tails	t-ai-l-s	
empty	e-m-p-t-y	y is an alternative spelling of the "i" sound.
apart	a-p-ar-t	
have	h-a-ve	ve is an alternative spelling of the "v" sound.
team	t-ea-m	ea is an alternative spelling of the "ee" sound.
huff	h-u-ff	
puff	p-u-ff	
all	al-l	
clever	c-l-e-v-er	

IRREGULAR WORDS. These are the words that don't follow the phonic rules completely. Usually, the consonants are regular but the vowels represent different phonemes. You'll need to teach your child how to pronounce these words and to recognize the unexpected parts. Here are the irregular words you'll find in this story:

are doing even goes guess he into of others pair pulls puts says
the their they to today watching what what's who's work you

ABOUT THE WORDS IN FAT CAT ON A MAT

Most words in *Fat Cat on a mat* can be broken down into single letters representing single phonemes (such as 'c-a-t' and 'y-e-l-p-s'). There are some words in this story, however, where a combination of letters creates a single phoneme, and these are listed below.

Word	Phonemes	Note
away	a-w-ay	ay is an alternative spelling of the "ai" sound (at the end of a word or syllable.
day	d-ay	
play	p-l-ay	
stay	s-t-ay	
bake	b-(a-e)-k	a-e is an alternative spelling of the "ai" sound. k is an alternative spelling of the "c" sound.
cake	c-(a-e)-k	
Jake	J-(a-e)-k	
snake	s-n-(a-e)-k	
bee	b-ee	
bees	b-ee-s	
flees	f-l-ee-s	
sees	s-ee-s	
tree	t-r-ee	
trees	t-r-ee-s	
buzz	b-u-zz	
clever	c-l-e-v-er	

Word	Phonemes	Note
chicks	ch-i-ck-s	
catch	c-a-tch	tch is an alternative spelling of the "ch" sound
hatch	h-a-tch	
patch	p-a-tch	
crack	c-r-a-ck	
eggs	e-gg-s	
for	f-or	
or	-or	
good	g-oo-d	
groans	g-r-oa-n-s	
moans	m-oa-n-s	
her	h-er	
like	l-(i-e)-k	i-e is an alternative spelling of the "ie" sound. k is an alternative spelling of the "c" sound.

Word	Phonemes	Note
little	l-i-tt-le	le is an alternative spelling of the "l" sound (at the end of a word or syllable).
luck	l-u-ck	ck is an alternative spelling of the "c" sound
stuck	s-t-u-ck	
my	m-y	y is an alternative spelling of the "ie" sound
new	n-ew	ew is an alternative spelling of the "ue" sound.
off	o-ff	
sandy	s-a-n-d-y	y is an alternative spelling of the "i" sound.
see	s-ee	
shouts	sh-ou-t-s	
ssssh	-sh	one long "sh" sound.
with	w-i-th	
will	w-i-ll	

IRREGULAR WORDS. These are the words that don't follow the phonic rules completely. Usually, the consonants are regular but the vowels represent different phonemes. You'll need to teach your child how to pronounce these words and to recognize the unexpected parts. Here are the irregular words you'll find in this story:

are crazy lazy don't me no of says she the to today you

ABOUT THE WORDS IN SAM SHEEP CAN'T SLEEP

Most words in *Sam Sheep can't sleep* can be broken down into single letters representing single phonemes (such as 'g-o-t' and 'f-l-o-p-s'). There are some words in this story, however, where a combination of letters creates a single phoneme, and these are listed below.

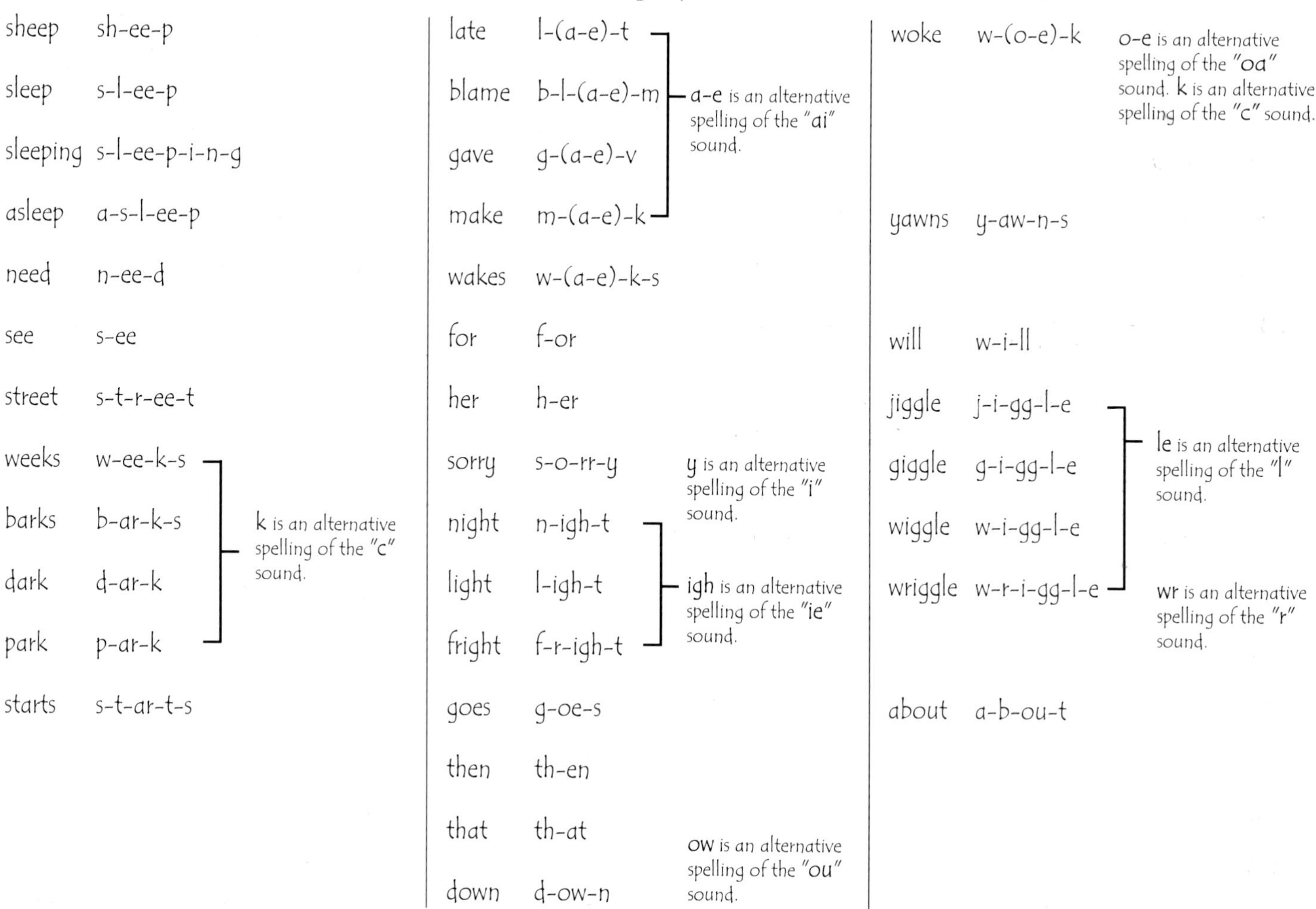

sheep	sh-ee-p	
sleep	s-l-ee-p	
sleeping	s-l-ee-p-i-n-g	
asleep	a-s-l-ee-p	
need	n-ee-d	
see	s-ee	
street	s-t-r-ee-t	
weeks	w-ee-k-s	k is an alternative spelling of the "c" sound.
barks	b-ar-k-s	
dark	d-ar-k	
park	p-ar-k	
starts	s-t-ar-t-s	
late	l-(a-e)-t	a-e is an alternative spelling of the "ai" sound.
blame	b-l-(a-e)-m	
gave	g-(a-e)-v	
make	m-(a-e)-k	
wakes	w-(a-e)-k-s	
for	f-or	
her	h-er	
sorry	s-o-rr-y	y is an alternative spelling of the "i" sound.
night	n-igh-t	igh is an alternative spelling of the "ie" sound.
light	l-igh-t	
fright	f-r-igh-t	
goes	g-oe-s	
then	th-en	
that	th-at	
down	d-ow-n	ow is an alternative spelling of the "ou" sound.
woke	w-(o-e)-k	o-e is an alternative spelling of the "oa" sound. k is an alternative spelling of the "c" sound.
yawns	y-aw-n-s	
will	w-i-ll	
jiggle	j-i-gg-l-e	le is an alternative spelling of the "l" sound.
giggle	g-i-gg-l-e	
wiggle	w-i-gg-l-e	
wriggle	w-r-i-gg-l-e	wr is an alternative spelling of the "r" sound.
about	a-b-ou-t	

IRREGULAR WORDS. These are the words that don't follow the phonic rules completely. Usually, the consonants are regular but the vowels represent different phonemes. You'll need to teach your child how to pronounce these words and to recognize the unexpected parts. Here are the irregular words you'll find in this story:

do does don't go I me says so the to what you

ABOUT THE WORDS IN TOAD MAKES A ROAD

Most words in *Toad makes a road* can be broken down into single letters representing single phonemes (such as 'g-o-t' and 'f-l-o-p-s'). There are some words in this story, however, where a combination of letters creates a single phoneme, and these are listed below.

Word	Phonemes	Note
Toad	T-oa-d	
Toad's	T-oa-d-s	
toads	t-oa-d-s	
road	r-oa-d	
roads	r-oa-d-s	
boasts	b-oa-s-t-s	
load	l-oa-d	
toast	t-oa-s-t	
goat	g-oa-t	
makes	m-(a-e)k-s	**ae** is an alternative spelling of the "ai" sound. **k** is an alternative spelling of the "c" sound.
make	m-(a-e)-k	
happily	h-a-pp-i-l-y	**y** is an alternative spelling of the "i" sound.
new	n-ew	**ew** is an alternative spelling of the "ue" sound.
house	h-ou-se	**se** is an alternative spelling of the "s" sound.
hill	h-i-ll	
will	w-i-ll	
spill	s-p-i-ll	

Word	Phonemes	Note
my	m-y	**y** is an alternative spelling of the "ie" sound.
waits	w-ai-t-s	
for	f-or	
or	-or	
truck	t-r-u-ck	
ticks	t-i-ck-s	
luck	l-u-ck-s	
stuck	s-t-u-ck	**ck** is an alternative spelling of the "c" sound. (truck – sticky)
track	t-r-a-ck	
black	b-l-a-ck	
sticky	s-t-i-ck-y	**y** is an alternative spelling of the "i" sound.
bring	b-r-i-ng	
brings	b-r-i-ng-s	
things	th-i-ng-s	
her	h-er	
time	t-(i-e)-m	**i-e** is an alternative spelling of the "ie" sound.
tired	t-(i-e)-r-d	
out	ou-t	
that	th-a-t	
that's	th-a-t-s	
then	th-e-n	

Word	Phonemes	Note
down	d-ow-n	**ow** is an alternative spelling of the "ou" sound.
with	w-i-th	
day	d-ay	**ay** is an alternative spelling of the "ai" soun
lays	l-ay-s	
eats	ea-t-s	**ea** is an alternative spelling of the "ee" sound.
party	p-ar-t-y	
Billy	B-i-ll-y	**y** is an alternative spelling of the "i" sound. (party – ready)
silly	s-i-ll-y	
ready	r-ea-d-y	**ea** is an alternative spelling of the "e" sound.
far	f-ar	
tar	t-ar	
too	t-oo	
steep	s-t-ee-p	
sheep	sh-ee-p	
need	n-ee-d	
see	s-ee	
except	e-x-c-e-p-t	**c** (before "e") is a alternative spelling the "s" sound.
wait	w-ai-t	
clears	c-l-ear-s	
steam	s-t-ea-m	

IRREGULAR WORDS. These are the words that don't follow the phonic rules completely. Usually, the consonants are regular but the vowels represent different phonemes. You'll need to teach your child how to pronounce these words and to recognize the unexpected parts. Here are the irregular words you'll find in this story:

comes everywhere I I'll into me no of one only rollers says she she's so the there's to today welcome what where you